JOY COWLEY

Giddy Up

Illustrated by Gaston Vanzet

Characters

Mr Speaks,
Movie Director

Cowboy
Joe

Cowgirl
Katie

Max
the Bandit

Sam
the Sheriff

Mr Speaks:
Okay, everybody. We're set to shoot the next scene. Are you ready, Cowboy Joe?

Cowboy Joe:
Ready, Director.

Mr Speaks:
Cowgirl Katie?

Cowgirl Katie:
I'm ready, Mr Speaks.

Max the Bandit:
I'm not ready. How can I be a masked bandit when my mask keeps slipping?

Mr Speaks:
Put a safety pin in it. Sam, give Max that safety pin.

Sam the Sheriff:
I can't. It's holding the star on my shirt. A sheriff has to have a star. Mr Speaks, I **need** this pin.

Mr Speaks:

I didn't get to be a movie director by fussing over safety pins. Let's get this show on the road. Katie, you and Joe ride into the desert. Max the Masked Bandit captures you both. Sam the Sheriff captures Max. Got it? Good. Let's roll. Lights, camera, action!

Cowboy Joe:
We'll jump on our horses, Katie, and ride away into the desert.

Cowgirl Katie:
Sure thing, Joe. But I hope we don't meet that mean critter Max the Masked Bandit.

Cowboy Joe:
Off we go! Oh beans! I hate this stupid horse!

Mr Speaks:
Cut! Cut! What's wrong now?

Cowgirl Katie:
It's these plastic horses. Why can't we have real horses?

Mr Speaks:
I told you! We can't afford real horses. This is a low budget film. That means no cash in the piggy bank. Got it?

7

Cowboy Joe:
Plastic horses don't move!

Mr Speaks:
That's okay. We'll jiggle the camera.

Cowgirl Katie:
They don't make a noise!

Mr Speaks:
You can make horse noises.

Cowgirl Katie:
How?

Mr Speaks:
Use your imagination.
That's what actors
do, isn't it? Lights,
camera, action!

Cowgirl Katie:
Mighty nice desert, Joe.
Gallopy, gallopy, gallopy.

Cowboy Joe:
Mighty nice weather,
Katie. Trot, trot, trot.

Cowgirl Katie:
Neigh! Neigh! Oh, Joe!
My horse has stopped.
It can see a shadow
behind that rock.

9

Cowboy Joe:
It's Max the Masked
Bandit! Let's get out
of here!

Max the Bandit:
Too late! Too late!
Put up your hands!

Cowboy Joe:
I don't believe this!

Cowgirl Katie:
Max is pointing
a cactus at us!

Mr Speaks:
Cut! Cut! I'll tell you once again. This is a—

Cowboy Joe, **Cowgirl Katie** and **Max the Bandit**:
—low budget movie!

Mr Speaks:
You got it! So stop whining and get on with the scene. Lights, camera, action!

Max the Bandit:
Get off your horses,
or you'll eat cactus
prickles.

Cowboy Joe:
Okay! Okay! Anything
but cactus!

Max the Bandit:
Now hand over
the payroll.

Cowgirl Katie:
Sorry, but there's no
payroll. We're broke.
Excuse me, your mask
just fell down.

Max the Bandit:
Thanks. It keeps slipping. No payroll? Then I'll tie you up and take you hostage. Someone will pay a big ransom for Cowboy Joe and Cowgirl Katie.

Sam the Sheriff:
Oh no you don't.
I'm Sam the Sheriff,
and your cactus doesn't
scare me. In the name
of the law, I arrest
you. Stand still while
I put these handcuffs
on you.

Max the Bandit:
They're not handcuffs.
They're rubber bands.

Sam the Sheriff:
Yes, I know. This is
a—

Max the Bandit:
—low budget movie.

14

Mr Speaks:

Cut! Cut! What's wrong with you actors? I didn't get to be a movie director by fussing about rubber bands. Sheriff, walk off with Max. Katie and Joe, ride back to the ranch. Camera, lights, action!

Cowboy Joe:

Yee-haw! That was a close call, Katie.
Trot, trot, trot.

Cowgirl Katie:

Saved from a loaded cactus, Joe.
Gallopy, gallopy, gallopy.